MACBETH

Adapted by Peggy L. Anderson & Judith D. Anderson

Cover Design by Nancy Peach

High Noon Books
A division of Academic Therapy Publications
20 Commercial Boulevard
Novato, CA 94949-6191

International Standard Book Number: 1-57128-319-6

14 13 12
10 9 8 7 6 5 4

Other attractive books in the Streamlined Shakespeare series are *The Taming of the Shrew, Romeo and Juliet, The Merchant of Venice,* and *Hamlet.*
Write for a free list of High Noon Books titles.

Table of Contents

ABOUT
WILLIAM SHAKESPEARE
(1564-1616)

William Shakespeare was born in Stratford-upon-Avon, a market town about eighty miles northwest of London. His father was a glovemaker and a trader in wool, hides, and grain. The family, which had eight children, while not rich, led a comfortable life. William was the third child in the family, and it is thought that he attended the Stratford grammar school where classes started at six or seven in the morning and lasted until five or six in the late afternoon. When the family's finances declined, it became necessary for him to leave school to go to work for a local tradesman.

He married Anne Hathaway when he was eighteen and she was twenty-six. They had three children, including twins.

It is not known exactly when or why Shakespeare left Stratford and moved to London where he quickly became involved in the theater both as an actor and a playwright. Theaters in London were closed from 1592 to 1594 because of the terrifying plague that swept throughout Europe, so Shakespeare spent his time writing plays and publishing two long narrative poems that immediately became popular and started him on the road to fame.

We can tell from the records of the number of properties he bought in London and Stratford that his income was more than ample. His days were busy acting at the Blackfriar and Globe Theaters and writing new plays to be performed there.

Shakespeare was only fifty-two when he died in Stratford. His birthplace and Anne Hathaway's cottage have been furnished to look as much as possible as they did in Shakespeare's time and are visited by thousands of tourists and admirers each year.

To this day Shakespeare's works can be found on stages in every country in the world. The work of no other playwright has been performed in so many nations throughout so many centuries. His friend Ben Johnson wrote in 1623, "He was not of an age, but for all of time." By now we know Johnson's observation was absolutely correct!

MACBETH

THE STORY

Prologue

This is a tale of howling witches, a mighty warrior and an ambitious wife. The witches in the story are scary, but the warrior and the wife are far more terrifying. The witches only plant evil seeds. The man and wife fertilize these with the blood of all in their path. Blind ambition brings about murder and madness. A hero falls from grace with a push from his wife. A queen's dreams melt into despair. And a reign of terror holds a country hostage. So goes the tragic tale of Macbeth.

Act I
Scene 1

Our story begins on a stormy night in Scotland. This proud country shares the island of Wales with its mighty cousin England. On this evening, a terrible storm was brewing. Sheets of rain were falling around three dark figures standing on a hill. Their shadowy profiles were framed by lightning. A purple glow lit the bleak countryside. The three figures were dressed in somber black with hoods tied loosely around their heads.

The first witch raised her voice, "When shall we meet again? In thunder, lightning, or in rain?" Her bushy eyebrows shaded her evil eyes.

The second witch, whose long matted hair flew in the wind, answered, "After the battle is over."

And the third witch, whose back was hunched, raised her wart-covered finger to the sky. In a rusty voice she said, "That will be when the sun sets."

"Where shall we meet?" asked the first witch with the evil eyes.

"In the empty field," replied the second witch with the wild hair.

"Where we will meet Macbeth," said the third witch with the hunched back and wart-covered fingers.

"I hear the toad calling us to our evil errand," cackled the second witch.

The thunder roared above. The rain fell below. And the evil three moved from sight, chanting, "Fair is foul, and foul is fair: Hover through the fog and filthy air."

Act I
Scene 2

A cross many fields far from the evil witches, a king and his aides were pacing nervously. When a figure was spotted in the distance, they gazed intently in that direction. As the figure drew closer, they could see he was covered in blood.

King Duncan asked, "Who is this bloody man? By the looks of him, he has been in the battle. He can give us a report."

The king's son, Malcolm, answered, "This is the good captain who saved me from enemy capture! Brave friend, give the king news of the battle."

The wounded captain told of the raging battle that had been led by Macdonwald. This rebel sought to overthrow King Duncan and rule Scotland. The captain described the blood-soaked battlefield where many had died. Had it not been for one brave man, the crown would have been lost. That brave man was Macbeth, the king's own cousin!

Macbeth, with the help of his captain Banquo, had saved Scotland. Duncan gave his thanks to the captain who was then taken to the doctor. As the wounded man left, two of the king's men, Ross and Angus, entered the camp. They had more to report from the field. They explained how the King of Norway had aided the rebels by providing fresh troops to renew the fight. This time the Thane of Cawdor had helped the Norwegians in the battle against the Scots. Once again, Macbeth had proved himself a hero. Sword to sword, he defeated the thane who was a traitor. Victory was claimed!

Duncan was pleased. He ordered the execution of the Thane of Cawdor. He also decreed that Macbeth would be given the traitor's noble title. Macbeth would now be known as Thane of Cawdor. He had earned this title by protecting the crown and his country.

Act I

Scene 3

O ut of nowhere came a thunderous clash. A cloud quickly covered the sun like a dark blanket. The thunder was deafening. And the lightning was threatening.

Over the hill came the three witches, each from a different direction. Their robes flew behind them like blackened wings in the wind. From above they appeared as vultures, drawn together by a newly killed prey.

The witch with the bushy eyebrows spoke first to the wild-haired witch. "Where have you been, sister?" she asked.

The wild-haired witch smiled to reveal a mouth of decayed teeth. She said, "Killing swine!" And she threw her matted hair back while shrieking.

The witch with the wart-covered fingers asked the evil-eyed witch, "And what about you, sister?"

The evil-eyed witch pulled her bushy eyebrows together. A single line of hair formed across her brow. It appeared as if a black cat's tail were suspended on her forehead. Raising and lowering the cat's tail, she told a story of evil doing. She had become angered when a sailor's wife refused to share some chestnuts with her. For revenge, she had put a deadly curse on the sailor's ship.

The sound of a drum roll was heard nearby. The evil-eyed witch interrupted her story. The cat's tail was gone as the bushy eyebrows separated in surprise.

"That's Macbeth coming," said the witch with wart-covered hands.

They quickly huddled together and began softly chanting,

"The weird sisters, hand in hand,

Posters of the sea and land."

Macbeth and Banquo were wearily making their way home when they came across this strange sight. Banquo looked more closely at the three.

"Who or what are you?" he asked after examining their strange attire and frightening faces.

"Speak, if you can!" commanded Macbeth.

The evil-eyed witch spoke up, "Hail, Macbeth, Thane of Glamis!"

The wild-haired witch then spoke, "Hail Macbeth, Thane of Cawdor!"

Finally, the wart-covered witch spoke, "Hail, Macbeth. Thou shall be king!"

Macbeth was confused by the witches' greeting. He told them that he was Thane of Glamis, but that he could not be Thane of Cawdor or king. Both of these men were alive and well. Macbeth did not know that the Thane of Cawdor was soon to be executed as a traitor.

"If you can see into the future," Banquo said, "tell me what you see for me."

The three witches glanced at one another. Then first witch spoke, "You will be less than Macbeth, but greater."

The second witch added, "Not so happy, yet happier."

Finally the third witch said, "Your children will be kings, but you will not."

Macbeth asked the witches to explain more, but they quickly vanished. The men were left in dazed silence. Where had the witches gone?

As Macbeth and Banquo discussed the witches' predictions, Ross and Angus rode up. Ross told Macbeth that he had been granted a new title. He had been named Thane of Cawdor as a reward for his heroism in battle.

"But the Thane of Cawdor is still alive. How can I have this title when he lives?" protested the confused Macbeth.

"He joined with the rebels and aided the King of Norway against Scotland. He has confessed to treason and will be executed," replied Angus.

Now Macbeth understood how he had earned his new title. Yet this news gave way to other questions. The witches' predictions about his new title had been true. Could the other predictions also come true?

Banquo began to worry about the predictions. He told Macbeth that he feared these predictions might tempt them to do wrong.

And, indeed, for a fleeting moment, Macbeth had thoughts of killing the king so he could take the throne. These evil thoughts frightened him.

"What are you thinking about?" asked Banquo.

Macbeth did not answer because he did not hear his friend.

Banquo saw that Macbeth was lost in thought. He observed, "He just needs time to become used to his new title. It is like wearing new clothes that don't fit well until they are worn for awhile."

Together the four men rode toward the king's castle in silence as the skies overhead darkened.

Act I
Scene 4

King Duncan and his sons Malcolm and Donalbain entered the dimly lit throne room. The furnishings in this royal room were sparse, as Duncan did not like lavish living. The sturdy wooden chairs had no soft cushions. The carpet was well worn like a royal river that had turned from regal green to murky brown. Thick dusty draperies hung in dark defense to the damp wind that blew in from the sea.

"Has the execution of Cawdor been carried out?" Duncan asked.

"Yes, he is dead," answered Malcolm. "Cawdor confessed his treason and died a noble death. Nothing in his life became him like the leaving it."

"I still cannot understand his treason," replied Duncan. "I trusted him absolutely."

Duncan's reflections were interrupted by the entrance of Macbeth, Banquo, Ross, and Angus. They respectfully bowed to the king.

"Cousin," said Duncan to Macbeth, "many thanks for all you have done. I owe you more than I can pay."

"My duties are to your throne," replied Macbeth.

"Banquo, you, too, are close to my heart," added Duncan.

Banquo nodded and replied, "Whatever I have is yours."

"I would like it to be known that I have decided that my eldest son Malcolm will be heir to my throne," announced Duncan. "May we all now go to Inverness and spend time with you in your castle?"

Macbeth was completely taken aback by Duncan's announcement. He tried to hide his shock.

"We would be honored by your presence," answered Macbeth. He hoped his voice did not betray his feelings. "I will go ahead to tell my wife of your visit."

"My worthy Cawdor!" said Duncan warmly.

Macbeth did not hear the king's words. Once again he was lost in his thoughts. "How can the witches' prophecy be true if Malcolm is to be king?" he wondered. Macbeth left the throne room confused and angry. There was a black cloud growing in his mind.

Act I
Scene 5

At Inverness Castle, Lady Macbeth had received a letter from her husband. In this letter Macbeth told her about meeting the witches and their prophecy. As she read, she became more excited. Her husband was destined to be king! She folded the letter and gazed out the window.

"He could be what has been promised, but I fear he will not," Lady Macbeth said. "He is too full of kindness." As Lady Macbeth peered out into the sunless afternoon, she thought, "I must find a way to force my will on him. Nothing must stand in the way of gaining the crown!"

When her husband returned to Inverness, Lady Macbeth greeted him with a warm embrace. "Great Glamis, worthy Cawdor," she said excitedly, "your letter has told me of the future."

"My dearest love," he replied, "Duncan comes here tonight."

"When will he leave?" asked Lady Macbeth. She needed to know how much time they would have for the bloody deed.

"He will leave tomorrow," answered Macbeth.

"He will never see tomorrow!" said Lady Macbeth. "The prophecy will come true!"

"We will speak further —-" said Macbeth.

"Put on an innocent face," she whispered into his ear. "Leave all the rest to me." And once more she gave him a loving embrace. Her mind was afire with dark plans.

Act I
Scene 6

The king and his royal party arrived at Inverness late in the afternoon. Lady Macbeth appeared at the entry of the castle to greet her guests. She cast a tall dark shadow on the steps of the castle as she stood surveying the group. The fading sun glinted in her fiery red hair as she made her way to Duncan. She smiled graciously at her king.

"And here is our honored hostess," said Duncan. "We thank you for your hospitality."

"We are at your service, your majesty," she said, smiling sweetly. She held out her graceful hands to extend a warm greeting to accompany her words.

Duncan took Lady Macbeth's hands into his own. "Where is the Thane of Cawdor?" he asked. "Take me to him that I may continue to show my favor to him."

Lady Macbeth bowed her head to her royal guest. Hand in hand, she led Duncan from the sunlight into the darkness of the castle walls. She clasped his hand tightly and looked straight ahead as Duncan followed her trustfully.

Act I
Scene 7

Inside the banquet hall, the servants were carrying huge platters of food and jugs of wine. The candles had been lit throughout the great room. Even though they burned brightly, the hall seemed shadowy. Outside, Macbeth stood alone in the courtyard.

"If only the deed could be done quickly," he whispered. "If it could be done without consequences." But his conscience reminded him that Duncan was not only his king. He was also his cousin and a guest in his home. He knew full well that murder was a horrid deed. Furthering his ambition was a poor excuse.

As Macbeth struggled with these demon thoughts, his wife entered the courtyard. Her dress of black satin whispered evil thoughts as she moved to him. What would his beautiful wife think of him if he did not follow through with the murderous plan?

"We will proceed no further in this business," he said firmly.

"What happened to your valor?" said Lady Macbeth angrily. "Are you willing to live your life as a coward? You are like the cat who wanted the fish, but was too afraid of the water!"

"If I kill the king, I am less than a man," protested Macbeth.

"You would be more manly to me if you were not so afraid!" cried Lady Macbeth.

"But what if we should fail?" he asked, feeling his

resolve give way.

"We fail?" echoed Lady Macbeth. "If you have courage, we will not fail." She then shared her murderous plan. "When Duncan falls asleep tonight, he will sleep soundly because of his hard day's journey. I will invite his two chamber servants to drink wine. They will become drunk and fall into a heavy sleep. This will leave Duncan unguarded for his murder, which will be blamed on his servants."

"If we put Duncan's blood on his sleeping servants and use their daggers, they will seem guilty," said Macbeth. "We will be seen as innocent." Macbeth was caught up in his wife's plan.

"No one would ever believe that we were involved," said Lady Macbeth. "Upon his death, we will roar with grief."

"I am now determined to go forward," said Macbeth. "I will put on a false face to hide my traitor's heart."

Thus, in a deadly play for power, Macbeth sealed his fate and that of his wife, and his good king.

Act II
Scene 1

B anquo and his son Fleance entered the courtyard of Inverness carrying a torch to light the way. The night was dark. The moon and stars could not be seen through the heavy fog.

"What time do you think it is, son?" asked Banquo.

"It must be after midnight, sir," answered Fleance gazing up at the sky.

"I feel very tired. Yet I don't think I could sleep. I'm afraid I would have bad dreams," said Banquo. As he spoke those words, he saw the shadowy figure of Macbeth enter the courtyard with a servant.

"You are not asleep yet?" asked Banquo. "The king has gone to bed. He is well pleased with your hospitality."

"If we had known he was coming, we would have done more for him," said Macbeth pleasantly.

Banquo told Macbeth that last night he had dreamt of the witches. He concluded that there had been some truth in their prophecies. Yet he was puzzled by some of the things they said.

Macbeth said that he had not thought again about the witches. However, he added, "If you give me your support when the time comes, you will benefit."

Banquo didn't like the sound of Macbeth's last words. What was his friend planning? They wished each other a good night. Banquo and Fleance left Macbeth standing in the courtyard under the starless night.

As Macbeth stood in the dark, he thought he could see the image of a bloody dagger in the air before him.

"Is this a dagger which I see before me? The handle toward my hand?" he cried out. He felt the power of an evil force, tugging at the sheath of his dagger. There seemed to be a force greater than himself that would have it no other way. Macbeth slowly pulled out the dagger. He heard a bell from within.

"I will go and it will be done," said Macbeth resolutely. "The bell invites me. Hear it not, Duncan. For it is a knell that summons thee to heaven or hell."

Act II
Scene 2

L ady Macbeth entered the castle courtyard and looked up to the sky. She searched in vain for the moon and stars. Her hair had fallen out of its net, framing her face like a lion's mane. She had drunk some of the wine that she had given to Duncan's servants. The effects had made her bold and brash. It had been easy for her to drug the servants and open the doors for the murderer.

What a night this was to be for them! They would seize the power that destiny had reserved for them. Visions of the dazzling crown she would wear were suspended when the shriek of an owl pierced the silence of the dark night. The owl's cry always signaled death, which meant that Macbeth had been true to his word!

"I have done the deed," said Macbeth as he entered the courtyard several minutes later. He walked as if in a trance with eyes fixed on his bloody hands. "Oh, this is a sorry sight!" he cried.

"That's a foolish thought to say. These deeds must not be thought of after they are done. It will make us mad," Lady Macbeth warned. "Get some water and wash the evidence from your hands," she instructed.

Lady Macbeth scolded him for returning with the daggers. He was supposed to have left them by the sleeping servants. Try as she might, she could not force him back to the scene of the crime. She had to return the daggers herself. Lady Macbeth smeared blood on

Duncan's servants and left the daggers beside them.

"My hands are now the same color as yours," she said to Macbeth when she returned from the murdered king's chamber. She stared at them curiously.

Then loud knocking startled the pair. They exchanged fearful glances.

"Quickly, we must put on our night clothes and pretend to be asleep," she commanded. "Do not be lost in your bad thoughts."

"I wish I could separate my deed from myself," he replied.

Then once again, there was the knocking. Louder and more demanding this time.

"Wake up Duncan with your knocking," Macbeth cried out. "I wish you could!"

Act II
Scene 3

O ne of the servants had finally heard the loud persistent knocking. When the heavy door was opened, Macduff and Lennox stood waiting. They had come to escort Duncan home. Hearing the voices, Macbeth went to see who was there. He offered to wake the king. Macduff declined, insisting it was his duty.

Macduff was gone for only minutes when they heard him cry out, "Oh, horror, horror!" He came running back into the room where Macbeth and Lennox stood frozen. "Go to the bed chamber. Do not make me speak of it. See for yourselves!" he said.

Macbeth and Lennox ran to Duncan's bed chamber. "Awake, awake, everyone!" cried out Macduff. "Ring the alarm bell. Murder and treason!"

The bell was rung. Shortly Lady Macbeth ran into the room.

"What is it?" she cried.

"Oh, gentle lady, this is not for you to hear," said Macduff. He could not bear to tell the beautiful mistress about the horror in her home. But when Banquo entered the room, Macduff could not hold back.

"Oh Banquo, our royal master has been murdered!" said Macduff.

"What, in our house?" shrieked Lady Macbeth with false surprise.

Commotion and confusion reigned throughout the great Castle of Inverness. Malcolm and Donalbain were awakened with the dreadful news.

The finger of suspicion pointed directly to Duncan's servants. They were covered with the murdered king's blood. The weapons were found on their pillows.

Unfortunately, further investigation of the servants was not possible. Macbeth had killed them in a fit of murderous passion as they lay sleeping in Duncan's blood. It was an act he said he regretted.

"Why did you do so?" Macduff asked suspiciously.

Macbeth defended his actions. He said that his love for Duncan had overcome reason. "Here lay Duncan. There were the murderers stained with his blood. How could I stop myself?" asked Macbeth tearfully.

Attention shifted to Lady Macbeth. She had fainted and needed to be helped to her room. Banquo, Macduff, and Macbeth left, swearing to avenge the bloody act of treason.

When Malcolm and Donalbain were alone, an uneasy silence fell upon them. What course of action should the sons of a fallen king take?

Malcolm spoke first. "It is easy for traitors to show sorrow they do not feel," he said. "I'm going to England."

"I'll go to Ireland," answered Donalbain. "Our separation will make us safer. These men's smiles hide daggers."

The royal brothers stole quietly to the stables. They embraced one another and then mounted their horses. As they rode through the land, their hearts burned with fury over the loss of their beloved father.

Act II
Scene 4

As Duncan's sons were riding swiftly through the Scottish countryside to safety, Ross, a nobleman, stood in front of the castle. He was thinking about the events of the last 24 hours. As he stood lost in his thoughts, an old man approached him.

The old man remarked that he had lived 70 years and had never seen anything as dreadful as the events of last night. Ross agreed with him.

"Good man," said Ross, "the heavens are troubled by a man's bloody act." He pointed to the darkened sky that should have been broad daylight given the time of day.

"Things seem unnatural," said the old man "just as the deed that was done."

"Did you hear that Duncan's horses broke down their stalls and ran away?" asked Ross.

"People say that the horses ate each other," replied the old man.

"It's true," said Ross. "They did, to the amazement of my eyes. Here comes the good Macduff." He asked his friend as he approached, "Does anyone know who killed Duncan?"

"It seems that his servants are guilty," Macduff answered.

"But what did they hope to gain for themselves?" asked the puzzled Ross.

"They were bribed," answered Macduff. "Malcolm and Donalbain have both fled. It makes them look suspicious."

"Then it's most likely that Macbeth will become king," said Ross.

The three men talked about Duncan's funeral and Macbeth's coronation in Scone. Soon the men bid farewell to one another and went their separate ways. Each man left with uncertain thoughts about what the future would hold for their homeland.

Act III
Scene 1

B anquo had entered a room in the palace at Forres, which was now Macbeth's residence. The royal couple had quickly moved from Inverness to the murdered king's castle.

"You have it all now," said Banquo to himself as he thought about Macbeth. "King, Cawdor, and Glamis—just as the witches promised. Yet I'm afraid you played most foully for it." Before he could ponder further, Macbeth and Lady Macbeth entered the room.

"Banquo, tonight we will have a formal supper," said Macbeth "and your presence is requested."

"My duty is to obey your command," said Banquo respectfully.

"Will you be riding this afternoon?" asked Macbeth curiously.

"Yes, my lord," said Banquo.

"Make sure that you come to our feast," said Macbeth.

"I will not fail to be here," said Banquo as he bowed to his new king. He had turned to go when the king began talking again.

"We have heard that our bloody cousins are now in England and Ireland. They have not confessed to killing their father," said Macbeth. "But they are telling people strange lies."

The two men looked at each other for several long seconds. Neither wanted to be the first to break the uncomfortable gaze. Finally Macbeth said, "Get to your horse. Good-bye until you return tonight. Will Fleance go with you?"

"Yes, my lord," said Banquo.

"May your horses be swift and safe," said Macbeth, drawing the last word out much longer than necessary.

Banquo left with a creeping sense of doom that he couldn't shake. After he mounted his horse, he took a good long look at Forres. He seemed to be searching for the solution to a puzzle. A puzzle that lay behind those castle walls.

Banquo had good reason to be concerned. Inside those very walls, Macbeth was meeting with two men. He was arranging for Banquo's murder.

Act III
Scene 2

Lady Macbeth was not enjoying her new royal title as she had imagined. "Nothing is gained when we have what we desire without joy," she thought sadly. As she sat beside her husband on the throne, she worried.

"Tonight you must be bright and cheerful to your guests," she advised him. There was enough suspicion already.

"Our faces must mask what is in our hearts," Macbeth said.

"You must stop this!" she replied.

"Oh, my dear wife, my mind is tortured," he said. "You know that Banquo and Fleance are still alive."

"They will not live forever," she said.

"They can be taken care of," he said. "A dreadful deed will be done."

"What is to be done?" asked his wife suspiciously.

"I want you to be innocent, dearest, until you can applaud the deed," answered her husband. "Wait and see. Once bad things have begun, they become strengthened by more evil," said Macbeth as he reached for her hand.

Act III
Scene 3

The two men were waiting in the bushes on a lonely stretch of road near Forres. Finally they heard the sound of hooves. The sound stopped abruptly as the riders dismounted and began to walk up the palace road.

"It's him," whispered one of the murderers.

"Get ready," said the other.

As the two unsuspecting men walked by the bushes, the murderers sprung into action. Their attack was brutal and swift. Yet Banquo knew in an instant what was happening.

"Oh, treachery! Fleance, run!" he cried out.

Young Fleance did not want to leave his father, but he obeyed. He could see that his father's wounds were fatal. Fleance ran through the cover of night as Banquo breathed his last.

"There's one dead, but the son is gone," said the first murderer. He knew that the king would not be pleased.

"We only did half of our job," said the second murderer.

"Let's leave and report what was done," said the first murderer.

They made their way back to the castle as Banquo lay bleeding under the moon.

Act III
Scene 4

In the palace, Macbeth was greeting his guests at the royal banquet when he saw one of the murderers enter the room. He approached him and whispered, "Is he dead?"

"My lord, I cut his throat for you," said the murderer.

Macbeth was visibly relieved. Then he remembered Fleance.

"You are the best of cutthroats," he said to the murderer. "If you did the same for Fleance, you have no equal!"

"Most royal sir, Fleance escaped," answered the man with his head hung low.

The anxiety rushed back like a herd of wild horses. Macbeth dismissed the man whose murderous mission had been only partially fulfilled. Once again he was trapped by his fears. He was standing in the corner wringing his hands when his wife approached him.

"My royal lord, you are not making your guests feel welcome," she scolded.

Macbeth did not hear his wife because he was intently watching the ghost of Banquo making its way through the crowd. The ghost appeared to know exactly where it was going. Gliding to the head of the table, it sat in the king's chair!

"Which of you has done this?" Macbeth demanded.

The hall grew very quiet as the guests looked uncomfortably from the king to one another.

"You cannot say I did this!" screamed Macbeth.

Seeing that the king was unwell, one of lords tried to dismiss the guests. The queen would not hear of it. She tried to explain away Macbeth's behavior, saying that he had these unusual fits since childhood. It would soon pass if ignored. No one in the hall really believed Lady Macbeth's explanation. Yet they could not leave when the queen insisted they stay. They returned to their eating and drinking, but with much less enthusiasm.

Lady Macbeth was furious with her husband. She grabbed his arm and pulled him aside. "Shame on you!" she said. "Why do you make such faces? You are only looking at an empty chair!"

"Look, see here," argued Macbeth as he pointed to the ghost of Banquo in his chair. "If the graves send back those we bury, we should leave them out for the vultures." The ghostly presence disappeared under Macbeth's pointed finger, leaving him stunned.

Lady Macbeth begged him to attend to their guests. Macbeth agreed to try to be a better host. He told his guests that his strange illness made him act in mysterious ways. Macbeth pleaded with his company to drink and be merry. He was starting to feel better when the ghost returned.

"Leave my sight!" he screamed at the wispy figure. "Your blood is cold!"

Again Lady Macbeth asked the guests to ignore her husband. When the ghost disappeared, Macbeth urged his guests to return to their seats. But everyone had enough for the evening. As they paid their respects to the king on leaving, Lady Macbeth could see distrust in their eyes.

When the king and queen were finally alone, the disappointment of the evening hung like a fog over their heads. Lady Macbeth was wearied by her husband's disturbed behavior.

Macbeth was worried about Macduff's absence at the banquet. Was Macduff disloyal? Tomorrow he would find out from his spy in Macduff's household. Macbeth was determined to root out all disloyal subjects. He would also seek out the witches again. He was desperate to uncover more about his future.

"I am standing in blood so deep that I cannot go back," he told his wife. His reign sprung from blood and must be sustained by continued bloodshed. It was the only way.

Lady Macbeth didn't protest, but there was fear in her heart. "You need sleep now," she said, though she doubted that any amount of sleep would help her husband. She had ignited his ambition. Now it was fueled by his own dark drive for power. Things were beyond her control. He had chosen his own course.

Act III
Scene 5

Macbeth's subjects were becoming increasingly
suspicious of their new king. After the banquet,
they could speak of little else but Macbeth's odd
behavior and the recent murders. They were beginning
to see connections that were very unpleasant. In a room
in the castle at Forres, such a conversation was taking
place between two lords.

The lords discussed the strange murders. They also
talked about Macbeth's probable role in these events.
"Duncan has died. And also Banquo. Are we to believe
that Fleance, his son, killed him? And Malcolm and
Donalbain also killed their gracious father?" Lord
Lennox asked. The other lord agreed that this was not
likely.

The two men also spoke of Macduff who had been
disgraced when he failed to come to the king's banquet.
He had fled to England to join Malcolm, who was seeking
help from the King of England to avenge his father's
death. There were also reports that Macbeth was
preparing for war.

This was only one of many such conversations that
could be heard throughout Scotland. There was growing
unrest, and the call for action would be heard soon.

Act IV
Scene 1

Hidden deep beneath the earth in a dark cave, a cauldron boiled noisily over a glowing fire. Outside cold sheets of rain fell in the darkness. Inside it was intensely hot as sparks whirled around the cauldron.

The three witches entered the cave, shuffling their feet as they made their way to the cauldron. They bent over the steaming pot with its foul odor seeping into every crevice of the cave.

They began to chant:

"Double, double, toil and trouble;
Fire burn and cauldron bubble."

When Macbeth came upon them, he demanded, "I need to know the answers to my questions."

The witches called forth their masters (mysterious apparitions) to answer his questions directly.

Amidst a great thunderclap, the first apparition appeared as an armored helmet. The voice cried out, "Macbeth! Macbeth! Beware of Macduff."

Another great thunderclap signaled the coming of the second apparition, which appeared as a bloody child. The apparition cried out, "Macbeth! Macbeth! Be bloody and bold for none born of a woman shall harm Macbeth." And then it was gone.

"Then live Macduff," said Macbeth, "for I have no reason to fear you." Then Macbeth reconsidered, " Yet just to make sure, you shall not live." His words gave testimony to the bloodthirsty monster he had become.

And a final thunderclap introduced yet another apparition to Macbeth. The third apparition appeared as a child with a crown on his head and a tree in his hand. The child broke the silence saying, "Macbeth shall never be killed until the great Birnam Wood comes to him at Dunsinane Hill." Then it vanished.

Macbeth clasped his hands to his heart and cried out, "That will never be. How could a forest pull up its roots and march? I shall live out my life as nature intended. Yet my heart throbs to know one thing. Shall Banquo's child ever reign this kingdom?"

"Seek to know no more," answered the witches.

"I demand to know," said Macbeth. "If you deny me this, an eternal curse shall fall on you!" He had to know this one last thing. To have power today was one thing, but his reign must also continue!

And together the witches said,

"Show his eyes, and grieve his heart;
Come like shadows, so depart."

A final apparition showing eight kings, the last with a glass in hand filed by. Banquo's ghost followed behind.

Macbeth rubbed his eyes. He couldn't believe what he had seen. He became enraged. "Filthy hags," he yelled. "Why did you show me this?"

"Yes, sire, it is so," said the first witch, "but why are you surprised?" The three witches joined hands and danced off into the night.

As Macbeth searched in vain for the witches, Lennox came upon him. He reported that Macduff had fled to England. Macbeth was furious that this enemy had escaped his clutches.

"From this moment on, I shall quickly act on my first feelings," vowed Macbeth. "I will go to Macduff's castle and kill his family."

Lennox said nothing, but wondered in silence. "Are there no limits to this tyrant's treachery?" he asked himself. It seemed not. He said a prayer for his country and the family of Macduff that would be Macbeth's next victim.

Act IV
Scene 2

U naware of the impending danger, Lady Macduff
and her children had just received a visit from her
cousin Ross. He told her that her husband had
fled Scotland in fear of the new king. Lady Macduff was
very upset. She believed her husband must be guilty of
treason.

"You must have patience," said Ross to Macduff's
weeping wife.

"He had none," Lady Macduff protested. "Our fears
make us traitors even when our actions do not."

"You don't know whether it was his wisdom or his
fear," said Ross.

"Wisdom! To leave his wife and children? He doesn't
love us," she cried.

Ross tried to comfort the sobbing woman by telling
her that Macduff was a noble man who knew best.
Promising to return soon, he left the woman alone with
her children who huddled around her.

Soon after, a messenger arrived to warn Lady
Macduff of approaching danger. He advised her to take
her children and leave immediately. Then he quickly left,
saying that he dared not stay longer.

Lady Macduff was not about to leave her home.
"Why should I flee? I have done no harm," she said.
These words had barely left her lips when several men
rushed into the room. The children were frightened and
started to cry.

"Where is your husband?" demanded one of the men.

"I hope that he is no place where you might find him," she answered bravely.

"He's a traitor," said the man.

"You lie, you hairy villain," cried Macduff's son.

"You are a traitor's child," answered the man. With those words, he took his dagger and stabbed the child.

"He has killed me, Mother," said the son as his little body fell to the floor. "Run away, I beg you."

Lady Macduff was already running through the halls with her baby in her arms. The king's men were close behind her in pursuit. A few minutes later Lady Macduff's agonizing screams echoed through the castle halls. Then the cries and screams of servants were heard. Finally all fell silent.

Act IV
Scene 3

In a palace in England, Malcolm and Macduff were discussing the sad affairs in Scotland. Their conversation was interrupted by Ross' arrival. They were pleased to see him and begged for news from home. Macduff desperately wanted to know about his wife and children. Ross told him that they were well when he left them. Then he quickly changed the subject. He told them of the men in Scotland who would be ready to join them in a battle against Macbeth when they returned home. Malcolm explained that the King of England had agreed to send 10,000 men to Scotland to fight against Macbeth.

As the conversation slowed, Ross admitted that he actually had bad news to deliver.

"If it is my bad news, do not keep it from me," said Macduff. "Quickly let me have it." His heart was pounding and his pulse had quickened.

"Your castle was attacked. Your wife and children were savagely slaughtered," said Ross.

The words rolled over Macduff like a huge weight of stone.

"My children, too?" he asked.

"Just as I said," replied Ross.

"Be comforted, " said Malcolm. "We will seek revenge."

"All my pretty ones? Did you say all?" asked Macduff again. His heart was broken. There was no reason to go on if all was lost.

"Face it like a man," said Malcolm.

Macduff struggled to accept the loss. Was it not his fault that they were killed? Why, oh why had he left them undefended?

"Bring me this enemy of Scotland and set him within a sword's length of me!" cried Macduff. If he could not protect his family in life, he could at least avenge them in death.

The men made the final plans to leave for Scotland the next day. This recent act of bloodshed fueled their desire to reclaim their country. Macbeth's evil reign must be overthrown at all costs. There had to be light at the end of this great darkness that had fallen on Scotland.

Act V
Scene 1

Outside Lady Macbeth's bedroom, a gentlewoman whispered with the doctor. They were talking about Lady Macbeth's strange nighttime wanderings. She had been sleep walking almost every night. She had also been talking in her sleep. But the gentlewoman would not reveal the words she had heard. Lady Macbeth came out of her bedroom carrying a candle. She walked by them without speaking. She appeared to be sleep walking again, but her eyes were fully open.

"Out, damned spot! Out, I say!" Lady Macbeth said rubbing her hands. "Who would have thought the old man would have so much blood in him?"

"Did you hear that?" asked the doctor.

"The Thane of Fife had a wife. Where is she now?" continued Lady Macbeth. "Will these hands never be clean?" She examined her hands curiously.

"She has spoken what she should not," said the gentlewoman.

"Here is the smell of blood still," she said. "All the perfumes of Arabia will not sweeten this little hand."

"This disease is beyond my medical skill," concluded the doctor. "She needs God more than she needs a doctor."

The doctor shuddered as he considered Lady Macbeth's words. And this was Scotland's queen!

Act V
Scene 2

Not far away from the Dunsinane Castle, the English troops, led by Malcolm, his Uncle Siward, and Macduff, were preparing for war with Macbeth. The Scots were arranging to join the troops at Birnam Wood.

It had been reported that Macbeth was fortifying the castle for the attack. Other reports said that he had gone mad. Those who obeyed him did so out of fear. The people were eager to purge the country of Macbeth and replace him with Malcolm.

Act V
Scene 3

Although Macbeth's officers had brought the reports to their king, he refused to be concerned about the impending attack by the English.

"Bring me no more reports," he commanded. "Until Birnam Wood comes to Dunsinane, I have no fear."

Just then a servant entered. His face was as white as a sheet. He reported to the king that there were 10,000 English men closing in for battle. Still Macbeth refused to be ruffled.

"I'll fight until my flesh is hacked from my bones!" he cried out. Then he noticed the doctor in the room. "How goes your patient, doctor?" he said, referring to his wife's health.

"She is not so sick, my lord," he answered, "but troubled by fantasies."

"Cure her of that," replied Macbeth. "Cleanse the heart of its burdens."

"The patient must help himself," answered the doctor quietly.

"Throw your medicine to the dogs," hollered Macbeth. He had lost his patience with those who could not do as they were commanded. "Tell me, doctor, what drugs would cleanse us of these English?"

The doctor said, " I see you are prepared for them."

"I will not be afraid of death until Birnam forest comes to Dunsinane," said Macbeth boldly.

The doctor shook his head. He thought to himself

that if he were lucky enough to be away from Dunsinane, nothing could tempt him to return.

Act V
Scene 4

Malcolm was readying his army in the countryside near Birnam Wood. He had decided on a plan to camouflage the army as it moved toward Dunsinane. "Let every soldier cut down a bough and carry it in front of him," he said. "This way we will conceal our numbers."

His soldiers began cutting down branches so each man could have a shield. As they worked, the men talked of the tyrant king and the reports that he planned to stay in the castle.

"It is his best hope," said Malcolm. "Many have abandoned him. He is alone except for those who fear him."

"Let us save our talk until the battle is over," said Macduff. "Fight like good soldiers.

And with that, the troops advanced toward Dunsinane.

Act V
Scene 5

A t Dunsinane Castle, Macbeth was giving orders to withstand the attack. "Hang our banners outside the walls," said Macbeth. "Our castle's strength will make the siege laughable. They will stay outside until the famine destroys them."

Macbeth was filled with confidence. He did not believe that the English could seriously threaten him. After all, Birnam Wood was miles away. Then he heard a strange crying noise.

"What was that cry?" asked Macbeth.

An aide who had just come into the room answered his question. "The queen, my lord, is dead," he said solemnly. He bowed and left.

"Out, out, brief candle!" said Macbeth. "Life's but a walking shadow." He had no tears for his wife's death.

A messenger entered. He was reluctant to tell the king what he had seen with his own eyes. "As I stood upon the hill, I looked toward Birnam. And I thought I saw the Wood begin to move."

The color drained from Macbeth's face. "Liar!" he cried loudly.

"Let me endure your wrath if is not so, my lord," he said. "You can see it coming within three miles."

"If you speak false, I shall hang you," said Macbeth. Then he said to himself, "I am beginning to lose my confidence." He was thinking of the prophecy, "fear not until Birnam Wood comes to Dunsinane."

"Ring the alarm bell! At least we'll die fighting," said Macbeth.

Act V
Scene 7

M alcolm, Siward, and Macduff lead their army to the front gate of Dunsinane Castle. They have disguised themselves with branches from the forest.

As they set down their leafy screens, Malcolm plans their strategy of attack. "Worthy uncle shall, with my cousin, lead the first attack. Worthy Macduff and I will do the rest."

The men vow to fight Macbeth unto the death. Siward says, "If we find the tyrant's army tonight, let us be beaten if we cannot fight."

With grim resolve Macduff states, "Sound all our trumpets. They are the announcers of blood and death."

Act V
Scene 7

Malcolm's troops engaged in battle with Macbeth's men. There was fighting and confusion all around the castle. Standing in front of the castle, Macbeth surveyed the battle. He had come out from cover to seek his fate. "I must fight until the end," he said. "Who is he that was not born of woman? That is the one I am to fear or none."

A lone soldier from Malcolm's troops approached Macbeth. It was young Siward. He looked at him curiously. "Who are you?" asked the soldier suspiciously. Macbeth looked him squarely in the eye and announced, "My name's Macbeth!"

Here was the hated tyrant. The murderous devil was before him. The young soldier engaged the old soldier with his sword. The youth fought bravely, but he was no match for the bloody Macbeth. Minutes after the fight had begun, young Siward lay bleeding on the ground.

Macbeth left the dead soldier and looked around for another to fight. He could see that his troops were losing the battle. He considered his next possible course of action.

"Why should I act like a foolish Roman soldier and die by my own sword?" he asked. "Better to attack others than myself."

"Turn around, hellhound!" a voice cried from behind. It was Macduff standing like a tower with the battle raging behind him.

Macbeth stared at the menacing figure. He felt his blood turn cold. This was the enemy he had sought to avoid. Rather he meet an army than this one man.

"Of all men, I have avoided you," said Macbeth. "My soul is too charged with the blood of your family."

"I have no words for you," cried Macduff. "My voice is my sword, bloody villain."

Macduff fought with the fury of one who was avenging his family's death. Macbeth fought with the confidence of one who was destined to win.

"You are wasting your effort," said Macbeth "for I cannot be killed by one born of a woman."

Macduff hesitated for a moment. "I was prematurely ripped out of my mother's womb," he answered.

At last Macbeth stood face to face with the witches' prophecy. Here was his fateful finish. "Cursed be the tongue that tells me this," cried Macbeth. "It has taken my courage away. I will not fight you." He pulled back his sword.

"Then you must surrender and live to be put on show," said Macduff. "We will treat you as one of our rare monsters with a sign saying 'Here may you see the tyrant!' "

"I will not surrender to kiss the ground of Malcolm's feet and be cursed by my people," said Macbeth with resolution. "Though Birnam Wood has come to Dunsinane and I am facing you who is not born of woman, I will fight to the last!"

Macduff gratefully accepted Macbeth's decision to fight to the end. With visions of his precious family in his mind, he fought boldly. He had failed to protect them in life, but he would not fail to avenge their deaths. Minutes later, Macbeth lay dead. His eyes were open and an expression of fear gripped his face. It was the fear of a mortal who would not escape judgment in death.

Macduff looked into those evil eyes and then held his sword high to the sky. A ray of sun reflected on the sword just before it was brought down heavy on Macbeth's neck. He mounted the head on his sword and carried it to his new king.

He knelt before Malcolm and bowed his head. "Hail, King! For that is what you are," he said reverently. "Here is the cursed head of the traitor."

The soldiers all cried out "Hail, king of Scotland!" Their beloved land was reclaimed. There would be no more innocent blood spent to purchase power.

The reign of terror was over. Peace and prosperity were enjoyed by all as Malcolm followed in his father's great footsteps.

MACBETH

THE PLAY

CAST OF CHARACTERS

DUNCAN, *King of Scotland*
MALCOLM, *Elder son of King Duncan*
DONALBAIN, *Younger son of King Duncan*
MACBETH, *Thane of Glamis*
LADY MACBETH, *Wife of Macbeth*
GENTLEWOMAN, *her attendant*
BANQUO, *Macbeth's friend*
FLEANCE, *Banquo's son*
MACDUFF, *Thane of Fife*
LADY MACDUFF, *Wife of Macduff*
SON OF MACDUFF

Thanes (noblemen):
ROSS
LENNOX
MENTEITH
ANGUS
CAITHNESS

SEYTON, *Macbeth's armor bearer*
CAPTAIN
AN OLD MAN
DOCTOR
1st MURDERER
2nd MURDERER
FIRST WITCH
SECOND WITCH

THIRD WITCH
SIWARD, *Earl of Northumberland*
YOUNG SIWARD, *his son*
GHOST OF BANQUO
APPARITIONS
LORDS, SOLDIERS, ATTENDANTS, SERVANTS,
MESSENGERS

Act I
Scene 1

Setting: An isolated heath in Scotland.

(Three witches enter. There is thunder and lightning.)

1st WITCH: When shall we three meet again?
In thunder, lightning, or in rain?

2nd WITCH: When the hurlyburly's done,
When the battle's lost and won.

3rd WITCH: That will be ere the set of sun.

1st WITCH: Where the place?

2nd WITCH: Upon the heath.

3rd WITCH: There to meet with Macbeth.

ALL WITCHES: Fair is foul and foul is fair:
Hover through the fog and filthy air.

(Witches exit.)

Act I
Scene 2

Setting: King Duncan's military camp near Forres.

(King Duncan, Malcolm, Donalbain, and Lennox with attendants enter with a bleeding Captain.)

DUNCAN: Who is this bloody man? By the looks of him, he has been to battle. He can give us a report.

MALCOLM: This is the good captain who fought courageously. He saved me from enemy capture! Brave friend, give the king news of the battle.

CAPTAIN: The outcome of the battle was doubtful. The two armies were very tired. They fought as two drowning men who cling to each other while sinking. The rebel Macdonwald was a villain who showed no mercy. But brave Macbeth with his smoking sword slashed him in two and chopped off his head.

DUNCAN: Your wounds and your words are honorable. Go, get him surgeons.

(The captain exits with an attendant.)
(Ross enters.)

DUNCAN: Who comes here?

MALCOLM: The worthy Thane of Ross.

LENNOX: He seems to be in a great hurry.

ROSS: God save the king!

DUNCAN: Where are you coming from, worthy Thane?

ROSS: I come from Fife where the Norwegian banners fly. Large numbers of Norwegian troops are assisted by the disloyal Thane of Cawdor in battle against us. Brave Macbeth confronted him in battle. Sword to sword, Macbeth won our victory.

DUNCAN: Great happiness! The Thane of Cawdor will not deceive us again. He must be executed. Macbeth will receive his title.

ROSS: I'll see it done.

(All exit.)

Act I
Scene 3

Setting: The heath.

(Thunder is heard. The three witches enter.)
(The sound of a drum is heard.)

3rd WITCH: A drum, a drum; Macbeth doth come.

ALL: The weird sisters, hand in hand,
Posters of the sea and land,
Thus do go about, about.
Thrice to thine, and thrice to mine,
And thrice again, to make up nine.
There the spell is done!

(Macbeth and Banquo enter.)

MACBETH: I have never seen a day that was so fair and foul.

BANQUO: What are these with withered faces and wild clothing? *(Points to the witches.)* They don't look like inhabitants of the earth.

MACBETH: Speak if you can. What are you?

1st WITCH: All hail, Macbeth! Hail to thee, Thane of Glamis!

2nd WITCH: All hail, Macbeth! Hail to thee, Thane of Cawdor!

3rd WITCH: All hail, Macbeth! That shalt be king hereafter!

BANQUO: (*To witches.*) Tell me the truth. Are you real or imaginary? You predict that my noble partner will have a royal future, but you say nothing to me. If you can see the future, tell me mine.

1st WITCH: Lesser than Macbeth, and greater.

2nd WITCH: Not so happy, yet much happier.

3rd WITCH: You will not be a king, but your children will be. So all hail, Macbeth and Banquo!

MACBETH: Stay and tell me more. By my father's death, I am Thane of Glamis. But how could I be of Cawdor? The Thane of Cawdor is alive, a healthy prosperous gentleman. And to be king is as unbelievable as to be Thane of Cawdor. Why did you stop us on this heath with this prophecy? Speak! I order you.

(Witches vanish.)

BANQUO: Did they vanish?

MACBETH: Into the air. They melted into the wind.

BANQUO: Were they really here?

MACBETH: Your children shall be kings.

BANQUO: You shall be king.

MACBETH: And Thane of Cawdor, too. Isn't that what they said?

BANQUO: Those are the words I heard. Who's there?

(Ross and Angus enter.)

ROSS: Macbeth, the king has happily received the news of your success.

ANGUS: We have been sent by the king to give you thanks. We are to bring you to him.

ROSS: The king ordered me to call you Thane of Cawdor. Hail, the title is yours.

BANQUO: What, can the devil speak the truth?

MACBETH: The Thane of Cawdor lives. Why do you dress me in borrowed robes?

ANGUS: The thane does still live yet he is under a death sentence, which he deserves. He joined with Norway and aided the rebels. He has confessed to his treason.

MACBETH: *(Aside.)* Glamis and Thane of Cawdor. The greatest is ahead! *(To Ross and Angus.)* Many thanks. *(To Banquo.)* Do you not hope your children shall be kings, since that was the prediction of those creatures who told me I would be Thane of Cawdor?

BANQUO: If we fully trust them, you may have desires to be king besides the Thane of Cawdor.

MACBETH: *(Aside.)* Why am I thinking thoughts so horrible that my heart is beating against my ribs? The thought of murder shakes my very soul.

BANQUO: *(To Ross and Angus.)* Look how lost in thoughts our friend is. Macbeth's new honors are like new clothes. They don't fit well until they have been worn for a while.

Worthy Macbeth, we are waiting for you.

MACBETH: I am sorry. Let us go to the king.

(All exit.)

Act I
Scene 4

Setting: King Duncan's castle at Forres.

(Duncan, Malcolm, Donalbain, Lennox, and attendants enter.)

DUNCAN: Is the execution done on Cawdor?

MALCOLM: Yes, he is dead. He confessed his treason and asked your pardon. He was deeply repentant. Nothing in his life became him like the leaving it.

DUNCAN: I could not tell by looking at his face what he was thinking. He was a gentleman on whom I built an absolute trust.

(Macbeth, Banquo, Ross, and Angus enter.)

(To Macbeth.)

Oh worthiest cousin! Many thanks to you. I owe you more than I can pay.

MACBETH: Allowing me to provide you with service and loyalty is payment enough.

DUNCAN: You are welcome here. And noble Banquo, you are no less deserving. Let me hold you to my heart.

BANQUO: Whatever I have is yours.

DUNCAN: My joy is great. Sons, kinsmen, and thanes, I want you to know that my eldest son Malcolm will inherit my throne. Let us go to Inverness and strengthen our bonds.

MACBETH: I will go tell my wife the joyful news of your visit.

DUNCAN: My worthy Cawdor!

MACBETH: *(Aside.)* This is an obstacle that lies in my path. It will cause my fall unless I leap over it. Stars, hide your fires! Let not light see my black and deep desire.

(Macbeth exits.)

DUNCAN: Macbeth is so valiant. He has gone ahead to prepare our welcome. Let us follow.

(All exit. Trumpets sound.)

Act I
Scene 5

Setting: Macbeth's castle at Inverness.

(Lady Macbeth enters reading a letter.)

LADY MACBETH: *(Reading.)   The witches met me on the day of our victory. When I tried to question them further, they vanished into air. As I stood in wonder, messengers from the king arrived and hailed me as "Thane of Cawdor." The witches knew this before I did. They also predicted that I would be king. I tell you this, my loving wife, so that you may rejoice. Greatness has been promised to me. Farewell.*

You are Thane of Glamis and of Cawdor. You shall be what is promised. Yet, I fear the weakness of your nature. You wish to be great and you have ambition, but not the evil to acquire it. *(A messenger enters.)* What is your tiding?

MESSENGER: The king comes here tonight. Our thane is coming with him.

LADY MACBETH: This is great news.

(The messenger exits.) Spirits, rid me of my womanly nature! Unsex me here. Fill me

with cruelty. Make my blood thick. Come, dark night and cover yourself with smoke from hell so my knife won't see the wound it makes. *(Macbeth enters.)* Great Glamis! Worthy Cawdor! Your letter has told me of the future.

MACBETH: My dearest love, Duncan comes here tonight.

LADY MACBETH: And when will he leave?

MACBETH: He will leave tomorrow.

LADY MACBETH: He will not see the sun tomorrow. Look like an innocent flower, but be a serpent under it.

MACBETH: We must speak further.

LADY MACBETH: Appear to be innocent. Leave all the rest to me.

(Macbeth and Lady Macbeth exit.)

Act I
Scene 6

Setting: Outside Macbeth's Castle at Inverness.

(Duncan, Malcolm, Donalbain, Banquo, Lennox, Macduff, Ross, Angus, and Attendants enter.)

DUNCAN: This castle has a pleasant setting. The air here smells sweet.

BANQUO: There are many swallows here. I have observed that wherever these birds nest, the air is delicate and pleasant.

(Lady Macbeth enters.)

DUNCAN: Here is our honored hostess. I am sorry for the trouble our visit may cause you.

LADY MACBETH: You have done so much for our family.

DUNCAN: Fair hostess, we are your guests tonight.

LADY MACBETH: All our belongings are at your disposal.

DUNCAN: Give me your hand. Bring me to our host whom we love greatly. *(Offers his hand to Lady Macbeth.)*

(All exit.)

Act I
Scene 7

Setting: Inverness Castle courtyard.

(Servers and Attendants enter carrying torches and platters across the stage to the dining hall offstage. They exit. Macbeth enters.)

MACBETH: Duncan is here in double trust. First, I am his kinsman and his subject. As his host, I should protect him from murder, not hold the knife. Besides, Duncan has been such a good ruler that his death will cause great sadness. I have nothing to spur me on except my ambition.

(Lady Macbeth enters.)

We will proceed no further with this business.

LADY MACBETH: What happened to your ambition? Are you afraid to be brave? Are you like the cat who wanted the fish but was too afraid of the water?

MACBETH: If I kill the king I will be less than a man.

LADY MACBETH: You were a man when you dared do it. Now that you have the opportunity, your courage is gone.

MACBETH: What if we should fail?

LADY MACBETH: We fail? Screw your courage to the sticking place and we'll not fail. When Duncan falls asleep tonight, he will sleep soundly from his hard day's journey. I will invite his two chamber servants to drink wine. They will become drunk and fall into a heavy sleep. His drunken attendants will bear the guilt for our great murder.

MACBETH: When we have smeared the blood on the sleeping attendants and used their very daggers, who wouldn't believe that they have done it?

LADY MACBETH: Who would dare believe otherwise as we shall roar with grief upon his death?

MACBETH: I am determined. Let us go. False face must hide what the false heart doth know.

(Macbeth and Lady Macbeth exit.)

Act II
Scene 1

Setting: Inverness Castle Courtyard.

(Banquo and Fleance enter with a torchbearer.)

BANQUO: How goes the night, boy?

FLEANCE: The moon is down, but I have not heard the clock.

BANQUO: I feel very tired. And yet I don't think I could sleep. I'm afraid I would have bad dreams.

(Macbeth enters with a servant bearing a torch.)

What, you are not asleep? The king is in bed. He was unusually happy and has sent generous gifts to your servants.

MACBETH: If we had expected his visit, we would have done more for him.

BANQUO: Everything went very well. Last night I dreamt of the three weird sisters. There was some truth in what they told you.

MACBETH: I think not of them. But if you give me your support when the time comes, you will benefit.

BANQUO: As long as I can keep my honor.

MACBETH: Meanwhile, have a good sleep!

BANQUO: Thanks, sir. I wish you the same.
(Banquo and Fleance exit.)
MACBETH: Go to my mistress. Tell her to ring the bell when my drink is ready. Then go to bed.
(Servant exits.)
Is this a dagger which I see before me? The handle toward my hand? Or is it my imagination? And now I see you covered with blood. You lead me in the direction I was going. My footsteps ring out the horror of my deed. While I talk on, he still lives.
(A bell rings.)
I go and it will be done. The bell invites me. Hear it not, Duncan. For it is a knell that summons thee to heaven or to hell.

Act II
Scene 2

Setting: Inverness Castle Courtyard.

(Lady Macbeth enters.)

LADY MACBETH: The wine that has made them drunk has made me bold.

(An owl shrieks.) Hark! It was the owl that shrieked. He is the fatal bellman who gives the warning bell before the execution. The doors are open. The drunken servants are snoring. I have drugged them so much that they are like the dead.

MACBETH: *(Macbeth enters carrying two bloody daggers.)*

I have done the deed. Did you hear any noise?

LADY MACBETH: I heard the owl scream and the crickets cry.

MACBETH: *(Looking at his hands.)* This is a sorry sight.

LADY MACBETH: A foolish thought to say a sorry sight. These deeds must not be thought of after they are done. It will make us mad. Go get some water. Wash this filthy witness from your hand. Why did you bring these daggers from the place? Take them back and smear blood on the sleeping servants.

MACBETH: I can't go there again. I dare not look at it again.

LADY MACBETH: You are too weak! Give me the daggers. If the king is still bleeding, I'll smear the faces of the servants with his blood. They must seem guilty.

(Lady Macbeth exits. There is a sound of knocking within.)

MACBETH: What is that knocking? Whose hands are these? All of the water in the ocean could not wash the blood clean from my hand. My hands would turn the sea from green to red.

(Lady Macbeth enters.)

LADY MACBETH: My hands are now the same color as yours.

(A knocking sound is heard within.)

A little water clears us of this deed. How easy this has been.

(A knocking sound is heard within.)

Hark! More knocking. Put on your nightgown so it will seem that we were asleep. Do not be lost in your bad thoughts.

MACBETH: I wish I could separate my deed from myself.

(A knocking sound is heard within.)

Wake up Duncan with thy knocking. I would thou couldst.

(Macbeth and Lady Macbeth exit.)

Act II
Scene 3

Setting: Inverness Castle Courtyard.

(A knocking sound is heard within. A servant enters and opens door. Macduff and Lennox enter. Macbeth enters and servant exits.)

MACBETH: Good morning to both of you.

MACDUFF: Is the king awake, worthy thane?

MACBETH: Not yet.

MACDUFF: He asked me to come by for him early.

(Macduff exits.)

LENNOX: Last night was very stormy. People said they heard strange screams of death. An owl screeched throughout the night.

MACBETH: It was a rough night.

(Macduff enters.)

MACDUFF: O horror, horror!

MACBETH and LENNOX: What's the matter?

MACDUFF: Go to the bed chamber. See for yourselves!

(Macbeth and Lennox exit.)

Awake, awake! Ring the alarm bell! Murder and treason!

(A bell rings.) (Lady Macbeth enters.)

LADY MACBETH: What is going on?

MACDUFF: Oh, gentle lady! 'Tis not for you to hear what I can speak.

(Banquo enters.)

Banquo, Banquo, our royal master's murdered!

LADY MACBETH: Woe alas! What, in our house?

BANQUO: Too cruel an act anywhere! Say it is not so!

(Macbeth and Lennox enter.)

MACBETH: If only I had died an hour before this happened. I would have lived a blessed life. Now the wine of life is gone.

(Malcolm and Donalbain enter.)

DONALBAIN: What is wrong?

MACDUFF: Your royal father's murdered.

MALCOLM: Oh! By whom?

LENNOX: It seems his servants did it. Their hands and faces were smeared with blood. So were their daggers found on their pillows.

MACBETH: I do repent that in my fury I killed them.

MACDUFF: Why did you do so?

MACBETH: My violent love for Duncan overcame my reason. Here lay Duncan, his silver skin laced with his golden blood. There were the murderers stained with his blood. How could I refrain?

LADY MACBETH: Help me please.

MACDUFF: Look to the lady.

MALCOLM: *(Aside to Donalbain.)* Why do we hold our

tongues?

DONALBAIN: *(Aside to Malcolm.)* We shouldn't say anything here. We also might be attacked.

(Lady Macbeth exits with help of servant.)

BANQUO: Let us meet and investigate this bloody deed. With the help of God I stand ready to fight against this treason.

MACDUFF: And so do I.

MACBETH: Let's dress quickly and meet together in the hall.

(All exit except Malcolm and Donalbain.)

MALCOLM: Let's not join them. It is easy for a traitor to show unfelt sorrow. I'll go to England.

DONALBAIN: I'll go to Ireland. Our separation will make us safer. These men's smiles hide daggers.

MALCOLM: Let's get to our horses and steal away. There is good reason for us to leave when there is no mercy here.

(Malcolm and Donalbain exit.)

Act II
Scene 4

Setting: Outside the entrance of Inverness Castle.

(Ross and old man enter.)

OLD MAN: I can remember 70 years well, but I have never seen anything as dreadful as this night.

ROSS: Good man, the heavens are troubled by a man's bloody act. By the clock, it is day. Yet the dark night has strangled the day's sun.

OLD MAN: It's unnatural, just as the deed that was done.

ROSS: Duncan's horses broke down their stalls and ran away.

OLD MAN: People say the horses ate each other.

ROSS: They did, to the amazement of my eyes. Here comes the good Macduff.

(Macduff enters.)

Is it known who did this bloody deed?

MACDUFF: The men that Macbeth killed.

ROSS: What did they hope to gain for themselves?

MACDUFF: They were bribed. Malcolm and Donalbain

have both fled. It makes them look suspicious.

ROSS: It's against nature! Then it's most likely that Macbeth will become king.

MACDUFF: He has already been chosen king. He has gone to Scone to be crowned.

ROSS: Will you go to Scone?

MACDUFF: No, I'm going home to Fife.

ROSS: I'm going to Scone.

MACDUFF: Well, I hope things are well done there. Good-bye.

ROSS: Farewell.

OLD MAN: God's blessings go with you.

(All exit.)

Act III
Scene 1

Setting: The castle at Forres.

(Banquo enters.)

BANQUO: You have it all now. King, Cawdor, and Glamis, just as the weird women promised. I'm afraid you played most foully for it. Yet, if they spoke the truth about you, then why shouldn't the prophecies be true for me? But hush, no more now.

(A trumpet sounds. Macbeth as king, Lady Macbeth as queen, Lennox, Ross, lords, and attendants enter.)

MACBETH: Tonight we hold a formal supper, sir. And I'll request your presence.

BANQUO: My duty is to obey your command.

MACBETH: Will you ride this afternoon?

BANQUO: Yes, my lord.

MACBETH: We have heard that our bloody cousins are now in England and Ireland. They have not confessed to killing their father. But they are telling people strange lies. We can talk of that tomorrow. Get to your horse. Good-bye until you return tonight. Will Fleance go with you?

BANQUO: Yes, my lord. It's time for us to depart.

MACBETH: May your horses be swift and safe. Farewell.

(All exit except Macbeth.)

To be a king is nothing unless I am safe. I fear Banquo. He is the only one I fear. The weird sisters said he would be father to kings. If this is so, I have killed the gracious Duncan for Banquo's children. I have given up my soul to make them kings!

Who's there?

(Servant enters with two murderers.)

Now go to the door and stay there until we call for you.

(The servant exits.)

MACBETH: Both of you know Banquo was your enemy. And so he is mine. What we are about to do must remain a secret business.

1st MURDERER: We shall perform what you command us.

MACBETH: It must be done tonight. It should be done some distance from the palace so there is no suspicion of me. His son Fleance must also share his father's fate.

2nd MURDERER: We will do it, my lord.

(Murderers exit.)

MACBETH: Banquo, thy soul's flight, if it find heaven, must find it out tonight.

(Macbeth exits.)

Act III
Scene 2

Setting: Another room in the castle.

(Lady Macbeth enters.)

LADY MACBETH: Nothing is gained when we have what we desire without joy.

(Macbeth enters.)

How are you, my lord? Why do you stay by yourself with your gloomy thoughts? What's done is done.

MACBETH: We are eating and sleeping in fear. We don't have the peace that we have given Duncan. He is in his grave sleeping well.

LADY MACBETH: Come, my gentle lord. Be bright and cheerful among your guests tonight.

MACBETH: I will, my love. So should you. Our faces must mask what is in our hearts.

LADY MACBETH: You must stop this!

MACBETH: Oh, dear wife, my mind is tortured. You know that Banquo and Fleance still live.

LADY MACBETH: They will not live forever.

MACBETH: They can be taken care of. A dreadful deed will be done.

LADY MACBETH: What is to be done?

MACBETH: I want you to be innocent of the knowledge, dearest, until you can applaud the deed. Once bad things have begun, they become strengthened by more evil. Come, go with me.

(Macbeth and Lady Macbeth exit.)

Act III
Scene 3

Setting: A road leading to the castle at Forres.

(Two Murderers enter.)

1st MURDERER: I hear horses.

2nd MURDERER: It's him.

1st MURDERER: They have dismounted.

2nd MURDERER: He will walk the last mile to the palace gate.

(Banquo and Fleance enter carrying torches.)

1st MURDERER: Get ready!

BANQUO: It will rain tonight.

1st MURDERER: Let the rain come down!

(They attack Banquo.)

BANQUO: Oh, treachery! Fleance, run, run, run. Revenge me!

(Banquo dies. Fleance escapes.)

2nd MURDERER: There's but one down. The son is gone.

1st MURDERER: We did half of our job.

2nd MURDERER: Let's leave and report what was done.

(All exit.)

Act III
Scene 4

Setting: The banquet hall of the castle at Forres.

(Macbeth, Lady Macbeth, Ross, Lennox, lords, and attendants enter.)

MACBETH: A hearty welcome to you all!

LORDS: Thanks to your majesty.

(The 1st murderer enters.)

MACBETH: *(To 1st murderer.)* Is he dead?

1st MURDERER: My lord, I cut his throat for you.

MACBETH: You are the best of cutthroats. If you did the same for Fleance, you have no equal!

1st MURDERER: Most royal sir, Fleance escaped.

MACBETH: Here comes my anxiety again. I am trapped by my doubts and fears. But I am safe from Banquo?

1st MURDERER: Yes, my lord. He's safe in the ditch.

MACBETH: Thanks for that. The grown serpent is dead. The young one who got away will grow up to be poisonous. For the present he has no teeth. Go now.

(The 1st murderer exits.)

LADY MACBETH: My royal lord, you are not making your guests feel welcome.

(The ghost of Banquo enters and sits in Macbeth's place.)

MACBETH: Thank you for reminding me. Health to all!

ROSS: Please grace us with your royal company, your highness.

MACBETH: The table is full.

LENNOX: Here is a place reserved for you, sir.

MACBETH: Where?

LENNOX: Here, my good lord. What is it that disturbs your highness?

MACBETH: Which of you have done this?

LORDS: What, my good lord?

MACBETH: You cannot say I did it. Never shake your bloody locks of hair at me.

ROSS: Gentlemen, rise. His highness is not well.

LADY MACBETH: Sit, worthy friends. My lord often acts this way. He has been this way since his childhood. Please keep your seats. The fit is only momentary. He will be well again. If you pay too much attention to his attack, he will be offended. Eat and pay no attention to him. *(To Macbeth.)* Are you a man?

MACBETH: Yes, and a bold one that would dare look on that which might frighten the devil.

LADY MACBETH: Oh, a fine thing is this! Shame on you! Why do you make such faces? You are only looking at an empty chair!

MACBETH: Look, see here! If graves send back those

89

we bury, we should leave the dead for vultures.

(The ghost disappears.)

LADY MACBETH: What is this folly?

MACBETH: There was a time that men whose brains were beaten would die. But now they rise again and push us from our chairs. This is stranger than murder.

LADY MACBETH: My worthy lord, your noble friends miss you.

MACBETH: I am forgetting. Do not be astonished by my behavior, worthy friends. I have a strange illness, which is nothing to those who know me. I'll sit down and have some wine.

(The ghost reenters.)

Leave my sight! Let the earth hide thee! Your bones have no marrow. Your blood is cold. You have no sight in your glaring eyes.

LADY MACBETH: Good friends, think of this as a sickness. It is nothing more, but it spoils the pleasure of the evening.

MACBETH: Leave, horrible shadow!

(The ghost vanishes.)

Now gone, I am a man again. Sit still everyone.

LADY MACBETH: You have ended the mirth and ruined the banquet with your fit. A kind good night to all. Go at once without regard for your rank and order.

LENNOX: Good night and may better health attend your majesty.

(All exit except Macbeth and Lady Macbeth.)

MACBETH: They say, blood will have blood. What do you say about Macduff's refusal to come to the banquet?

LADY MACBETH: Have you sent for him, sir?

MACBETH: Tomorrow I will. I have a servant in his household who is paid to spy on him. Tomorrow I will also go to the weird sisters. I am determined to know the worst. I am standing in blood so deep that I cannot go back.

LADY MACBETH: You need sleep now.

MACBETH: Come, we'll sleep. My strange self-deception tonight comes from the fears of a beginner. We are just beginning our deed.

(Macbeth and Lady Macbeth exit.)

Act III
Scene 5

Setting: A room in the castle at Forres.

(Lennox and another lord enter.)

LENNOX: Very strange things have happened. Duncan has died. And also Banquo. Are we to believe that Fleance, his son, killed him? And Malcolm and Donalbain also killed their gracious father? How Macbeth grieved over the death of Duncan! Did he not immediately kill the two suspects that were slaves of a drunken stupor? Wasn't that a noble deed? And wise, too. For it would have angered anyone with a heart to hear the men deny the crime. He has managed things quite well. I hear that Macduff has been disgraced because he failed to come to the tyrant's feast.

LORD: Duncan's son now lives at the English court. Macduff has gone there to ask for aid. This made Macbeth so angry he is preparing for war.

LENNOX: Did he send for Macduff?

LORD: He did, but Macduff refused to come.

LENNOX: Hopefully he may return soon to our suffering country.

LORD: I'll send my prayers to him.

(Lennox and lord exit.)

Act IV
Scene 1

Setting: A cave with a boiling cauldron in the middle.

(Sound of thunder. Three witches enter.)

1st WITCH: Round about the cauldron go;
In the poisoned entrails throw.

ALL: Double, double, toil and trouble;
Fire burn and cauldron bubble.

2nd WITCH:Eye of newt, and toe of frog,
Wool of bat, and tongue of dog,
For a charm of powerful trouble,
Let a hell-broth boil and bubble.

ALL: Double, double, toil and trouble;
Fire burn and cauldron bubble.

2nd WITCH:Cool it with a baboon's blood,
Then the spell is firm and good.

(Macbeth enters.)

MACBETH: I need to know the answers to my questions.

ALL: Come high or low; yourself and show.
(Thunder is heard. 1st apparition appears: an armored-head.)

1st APPARITION: Macbeth! Macbeth! Beware of

Macduff! Beware of the Thane of Fife!

(1st apparition descends.)

MACBETH: Whatever you are, thank you for the warning. But one more word—-

(Thunder is heard. 2nd apparition appears: a child covered with blood.)

2nd APPARITION: Macbeth! Macbeth! Be bloody, bold and resolute. Laugh to scorn the power of man. For none of woman born shall harm Macbeth.

(Apparition descends.)

MACBETH: Then live, Macduff. Why should I fear you? Yet, just to guarantee my safety, you shall not live.

(Thunder is heard. 3rd apparition appears: a child crowned, with a tree in his hand.)

3rd APPARITION: Macbeth shall never be killed until Great Birnam Wood come against him to Dunsinane Hill. *(Apparition descends.)*

MACBETH: That will never be. How could a forest pull its roots up and march? I shall live out my life as nature intended. Yet my heart throbs to know one thing. Shall Banquo's child ever reign this kingdom?

ALL: Seek to know no more.

MACBETH: I demand to know. If you deny me this, an eternal curse shall fall on you. Let me know—-

(The cauldron descends.)

ALL: Show his eyes. Grieve his heart; Come like shadows, so depart.

(A parade of eight kings appears, the last with a glass in his hand. Banquo's ghost follows.)

MACBETH: Filthy hags! Why do you show me this? Will the line stretch out to eternity? I'll see no more. Now I know it's true, for bloody Banquo smiles at me and points at the kings as his. Is this so?

(The apparitions disappear.)

1st WITCH: Yes, sire all this is so. But why are you so amazed? Come, sisters, let's cheer him up.

(Music is heard, and the witches dance and then vanish.)

MACBETH: Let this evil hour stand forever cursed on the calendar.

(Lennox enters.)

MACBETH: Did you see the weird sisters?

LENNOX: No, my lord.

MACBETH: I heard galloping horses. Who was it?

LENNOX: Messengers. Macduff has fled to England.

MACBETH: Fled to England!

LENNOX: Yes, my good lord.

MACBETH: From this moment on, I shall quickly act on my first feelings. I will go to the castle of Macduff, seize Fife and kill his wife and children. And all his kin. I'll do this with a cool temper.

(Macbeth and Lennox exit.)

Act IV
Scene 2

Setting: Macduff's castle in Fife.

(Lady Macduff, her son, and Ross enter.

LADY MACDUFF: Why did he leave the country?

ROSS: You must have patience, madam.

LADY MACDUFF: He had none. His flight was madness. Our fears make us traitors even when our actions do not.

ROSS: You don't know whether it was his wisdom or his fear.

LADY MACDUFF: Wisdom? To leave his wife and children. He doesn't love us.

ROSS: My dearest cousin, your husband is noble and wise. He knows best. I dare not speak further. I must take leave of you. I shall be back here again before long.

(Ross exits.)

LADY MACDUFF: Sirrah, your father's dead.

SON: My father is not dead in spite of what you are saying.

LADY MACDUFF: Yes, he is dead. What will you do for a father?

97

SON: What will you do for a husband?

LADY MACDUFF: Why, I can buy myself twenty at any market.

SON: Then you'll buy them to sell again.

LADY MACDUFF: You speak as a clever child.

SON: Was my father a traitor, mother?

LADY MACDUFF: Yes, that he was.

(A messenger enters.)

MESSENGER: Bless you, fair lady. I believe some danger is approaching you. Please take my advice and leave from here with your little ones. I dare not stay longer.

(Messenger exits.)

LADY MACDUFF: Why should I flee? I have done no harm.

(Murderers enter.)

MURDERER: Where is your husband?

LADY MACDUFF: I hope he is in no place where you might find him.

MURDERER: He's a traitor.

SON: You lie, you hairy villain.

MURDERER: You traitor's child!

(Stabs child.)

SON: He has killed me, Mother. Run away, I beg you!

(Child dies.)

(Lady Macduff exits crying 'murder!' She is chased by the murderers.)

Act IV
Scene 3

Setting: King Edward's palace in England.

(Macduff and Malcolm enter.)

MALCOLM: Let's find some dark place where we can weep.

MACDUFF: Instead, let us take our swords like good men and defend our fallen country.

(Ross enters.)

MACDUFF: Look who's coming! My gentle cousin. Is Scotland still standing as it was?

ROSS: Yes, good men are dying before their time.

MACDUFF: How is my wife? And all my children?

ROSS: They were at peace when I left them.

MACDUFF: Don't be so stingy with your news. Tell us everything.

ROSS: There is a rumor that many worthy men are ready to fight.

MALCOLM: Let them be comforted. We are coming. Gracious England has lent us Siward and ten thousand men.

ROSS: I wish I could answer with similar comfort,

but I have bad news.

MACDUFF: If it is my bad news, do not keep it from me.

ROSS: Your castle was attacked, and your wife and children were savagely slaughtered.

MALCOLM: Merciful heaven!

MACDUFF: My children, too?

ROSS: Wife, children, servants, and all that could be found.

MACDUFF: And I was away! My wife killed, too?

ROSS: Just as I said.

MALCOLM: Be comforted. We will make medicine of our revenge to cure this deadly grief.

MACDUFF: He has no children. All my pretty ones? All my pretty chicks and their mother killed in one fell swoop?

MALCOLM: Face it like a man.

MACDUFF: I shall do so, but I must also feel it like a man.

MALCOM: Let your grief sharpen your sword.

MACDUFF Bring me this fiend of Scotland and set him within a sword's length of me!

MALCOLM: Come, our troops are ready. The night is long that never finds the day.

(All exit.)

Act V
Scene 1

Setting: A room in Dunsinane castle.

(A doctor and a gentlewoman enter.)

DOCTOR: This is very unnatural. To have the benefit of sleep and act wide awake. During this state, have you at any time heard her say anything?

GENTLEWOMAN: That, sire, I cannot report on.

DOCTOR: You may tell me. And you should.

GENTLEWOMAN: I cannot tell anyone.

(Lady Macbeth enters carrying a candle.)

DOCTOR: Her eyes are open.

GENTLEWOMAN: Yes, but she sees nothing.

DOCTOR: What is she doing? Look, how she rubs her hands.

GENTLEWOMAN: It is her accustomed action to seem to be washing her hands.

LADY MACBETH: Out, damned spot! Out, I say! One; two: why then 'tis time to do it. What need we fear who knows it? None can challenge our power. Yet who would have thought the old man to have so much blood in him?

DOCTOR: Did you hear that?

101

LADY MACBETH: The Thane of Fife had a wife. Where is she now? What, will these hands never be clean?

DOCTOR: You have learned what you should not.

GENTLEWOMAN: She has spoken what she should not. I am sure of that.

LADY MACBETH: Here's the smell of the blood still. All the perfumes of Arabia will not sweeten this little hand.

DOCTOR: This disease is beyond my medical skill.

LADY MACBETH: Wash your hands. Put on your nightgown. Look not so pale. I tell you again. Banquo's buried. He cannot come out of his grave. To bed, to bed. There's knocking at the gate. What's done cannot be undone.

(Lady Macbeth exits.)

DOCTOR: She needs God more than she needs a doctor. Look after her. So, good night.

GENTLEWOMAN: Good night, good doctor.

(Doctor and gentlewoman exit.)

Act V

Scene 2

Setting: The country near Dunsinane.

(The sound of a drum is heard. Menteith, Caithness, Angus, Lennox, and soldiers enter.)

MENTEITH: The English army is nearby. It is led by Malcolm, his Uncle Siward, and the good Macduff.

ANGUS: We shall meet them near Birnam Wood.

MENTEITH: What is the tyrant doing?

CAITHNESS: He is strongly fortifying Dunsinane. Some say he has gone mad. Others who hate him less say he is in a brave fury.

ANGUS: Now he feels his secret murders are sticking to his hands. Those who obey him, do so only from fear, not from love.

MENTEITH: Who could blame him for his tormented feelings of fear and disgust?

LENNOX: We need to make our true king blossom, and drown out the weeds. Let's march toward Birnam.

(All exit marching.)

Act V

Scene 3

Setting: A court in the Castle Dunsinane.

(Macbeth, doctor, and attendants enter.)

MACBETH: Bring me no more reports. Until Birnam Wood comes to Dunsinane, I have no fear. The spirits have told me 'Fear not, Macbeth, no man that's born of woman shall have power over thee.' So fly away, false thanes, and join the soft English.

(A servant enters.)

Where did you get that goose look?

SERVANT: There are ten thousand.

MACBETH: Geese, villain?

SERVANT: Soldiers, sir.

MACBETH: Go prick your face to get some red in it, you lily-livered boy! What soldiers are these?

SERVANT: The English force.

MACBETH: Take your face away. Seyton!

(Servant exits.) (Seyton enters.)

SEYTON: What is your gracious pleasure?

MACBETH: What is the news?

SEYTON: That which was reported is confirmed.

MACBETH: I'll fight until my flesh is hacked from my bones. Give me my armor. *(To doctor.)* How goes your patient?

DOCTOR: Not so sick, my lord, but troubled by fantasies that keep her from rest.

MACBETH: Cure her of that. Can't you cure a diseased mind? Cleanse the heart of its burdens?

DOCTOR: The patient must help himself.

MACBETH: Throw your medicine to the dogs. I'll have none of it. What drugs would cleanse us of these English? Do you hear them?

DOCTOR: Ay, my good lord.

MACBETH: I will not be afraid of death till Birnam forest comes to Dunsinane.

(Macbeth, Seyton, and attendants exit.)

DOCTOR: If I were away from Dunsinane, nothing could tempt me to return.

(Doctor exits.)

Act V
Scene 4

Setting: Countryside near Birnam Wood.

(Sound of drums is heard. Malcolm, Siward and his son, Young Siward, Macduff, Menteith, Caithness, Angus, Lennox, Ross, and soldiers enter marching.)

MALCOLM: I hope that the day is at hand when we will once again be safe in our homes.

SIWARD: What wood is this before us?

MENTEITH: The Wood of Birnam.

MALCOLM: Let every soldier cut down a bough and carry it in front of him. Thereby we will conceal our numbers.

SOLDIER: It shall be done.

SIWARD: We have heard that the confident tyrant will stay in Dunsinane.

MALCOLM: It is his best hope. Many who have served him have now left him. And those who serve him have no loyalty in their hearts.

MACDUFF: Let us save our talk until after the battle is over. Fight like good soldiers.

SIWARD: The time approaches when we will know

whether we can achieve what we hope for. Have the army advance the war.

(All exit marching.)

Act V
Scene 5

Setting: The court of Dunsinane Castle.

(Macbeth, Seyton, and soldiers enter with drums and flags.)

MACBETH: Hang our banners on the outside walls. They will stay outside until famine destroys them. If we had not so many deserters, we could have met them face to face.

(A cry of women is heard.)

What is that noise?

SEYTON: It is the cry of women, my good lord. The queen is dead.

MACBETH: Out, out, brief candle! Life is but a walking shadow. A poor player that struts and frets his hour upon the stage and then is heard no more. It is a tale told by an idiot, full of sound and fury, signifying nothing.

(A messenger enters.)

MESSENGER: Gracious my lord, I should report that which I saw. But I do not know how to do it.

MACBETH: Well, say it, sir.

MESSENGER: As I did stand my watch upon the hill, I looked toward Birnam and I thought the wood began to move.

MACBETH: Liar!

MESSENGER: Let me endure your wrath if it is not so. You can see it coming within three miles away. I say it is a moving grove.

MACBETH: If you speak false, I shall hang you. I am beginning to lose my confidence. "Fear not, till Birnam Wood come to Dunsinane." And now a wood is coming to Dunsinane. Ring the alarm bell! At least we'll die fighting!

(All exit.)

Act V
Scene 6

Setting: In front of the Dunsinane Castle gate.

(Malcolm, Siward, and Macduff enter with their army covered with branches.)

MALCOLM: Now we're near enough. You may throw down your leafy screens. Worthy uncle shall with my cousin lead the first attack. Worthy Macduff and I will do the rest.

SIWARD: Farewell. If we find the tyrant's army tonight, let us be beaten if we cannot fight.

MACDUFF: Sound all our trumpets. They are the announcers of blood and death.

(All exit.)

Act V
Scene 7

Setting: In front of the Dunsinane Castle gate.

(Macbeth enters.)

MACBETH: I must fight until the end. Who is he that was not born of woman? That is the one I am to fear or none.

(Young Siward enters.)

YOUNG SIWARD: What is thy name?

MACBETH: My name's Macbeth.

YOUNG SIWARD: The devil himself could not pronounce a title that is more hateful to my ear!

MACBETH: Nor more fearful.

YOUNG SIWARD: You lie, hated tyrant! With my sword I'll prove that you lie!

(They fight and Young Siward is killed.)

MACBETH: You were born of a woman. I smile at the swords of men who were born of woman.

(Macbeth exits.)

(Trumpets sound. Macduff enters.)

MACDUFF: The noise came from this way. Tyrant, show

your face! If you have been killed by another's sword, the ghosts of my wife and children will haunt me. Fortune, let me find him. I beg for nothing more.

(Malcolm and Siward enter.)

SIWARD: My lord, the castle has surrendered without resistance. The noble thanes have fought bravely. Victory is almost yours. Enter the castle, sir.

(All exit.)

(Macbeth enters.)

MACBETH: Why should I act like a foolish Roman and die by my own sword? I see living bodies that the gashes would look better on.

(Macduff enters.)

MACDUFF: Turn around hellhound!

MACBETH: Of all men, I have avoided you. My soul is too charged with the blood of yours already.

MACDUFF: I have no words for you. My voice is my sword, bloody villain!

(They fight.)

MACBETH: You are wasting your effort. Let your blade fall on those who are vulnerable. I cannot be killed by one born of a woman.

MACDUFF: Lose hope in your magic spell. Let the angel tell you that Macduff was prematurely ripped out of his mother's womb.

MACBETH: Cursed be the tongue that tells me this! It hath taken my courage away. I will not fight you.

MACDUFF: Then surrender, coward and live to be put

on show. We will treat you as one of our rare monsters, with a sign, 'Here may you see the tyrant.'

MACBETH: I will not surrender to kiss the ground of young Malcolm's feet and to be cursed by the crowds. Though Birnam Wood come to Dunsinane and I am facing you who are not of woman born, I will fight to the last.

(Macduff and Macbeth exit fighting. They re-enter fighting. Macbeth is slain.)

(Malcolm, Siward, Ross, thanes, and soldiers enter carrying drums and flags.)

MALCOLM: I wish our friends had safely arrived.

SIWARD: Some must be dead. Yet, victory was cheaply won today.

MALCOLM: Macduff is still missing, and your noble son.

ROSS: Your son, my lord, has paid a soldier's debt. He died like a man.

SIWARD: Why then, he is God's soldier now. I could not wish for a fairer death. His funeral bell has rung.

(Macduff enters with Macbeth's head.)

MACDUFF: Hail, king! For that is what you are. Here is the cursed head of the tyrant. Hail, King of Scotland!

ALL: Hail, King of Scotland!

MALCOLM: We shall repay you all for your loyalty. My thanes and kinsmen, from this time forward you are all earls. We will call home our exiled friends abroad. We will punish the cruel ministers of this dead butcher and his fiendish wife. So thanks to all and each one whom we invite to Scone where we shall be crowned.

(All exit.)

THE GLOBE THEATER

The Globe Theater may well be the most famous theater in the world, for it was here that Shakespeare and other literary giants of his day produced their plays and other dramatic works.

Shakespeare and several other well-known actors needed a place to perform and so they pooled their funds and designed and built the Globe in 1599. Since they were theatrical professionals in every sense of the word, the building fit their needs perfectly. The Globe was octagonally-shaped with a roofless inner pit into which the stage projected. Three galleries (balconies) rose one above the other, the topmost of which had a thatched roof. One day, in order to provide reality in a production of Shakespeare's *King Henry the Eighth*, a cannon was discharged. Unfortunately, this piece of stagecraft set fire to the thatched roof, and the entire building burned. It was rebuilt the following year but was torn down 30 years later by the Puritans, who needed the space for houses.

A new Globe Theater was recently completed in London. Only materials that would have been found in the original Globe were used, a perfect setting to enjoy Shakespeare's genius.

About the Editors

Peggy L. Anderson, PhD, is a professor and Special Education Program Coordinator at Metropolitan State College of Denver. She has taught students with learning disabilities at the elementary and middle school levels in South Carolina and Florida. Her master's degree is from the Citadel and her doctorate is from the University of Denver. She completed her postdoctoral work with the Department of Pediatrics at Johns Hopkins University. Her research interests have focused on language-learning disabilities, dyslexia, and inclusion issues.

Judith D. Anderson, JD, is a trial attorney in southern California, specializing in the defense of school districts. She has taught Shakespeare to high school students in the United States and the United Kingdom for ten years. As a Fullbright Scholar, she travelled extensively in the British Isles, and met with the Queen Mother of England. She received her bachelor's degree at Flagler College and her law degree at Southwestern University School of Law.